Health and Safety Executive

Health and Safety series booklet HS(G)31

machines

Contents

London: Her Majesty's Stationery Office

HS(G) series
The purpose of this series is to provide guidance for those
who have duties under the Health and Safety at Work etc Act
1974 and other relevant legislation. It gives guidance on the
dangers associated with the machine - making of pies and
tarts and the safeguards to be used to avoid accidents but it
should not be regarded as an authoritative interpretation of the
law.

Further advice on this or any other HSE publications may be
obtained from Area Offices of HSE or from the general
enquiry points listed below.

Health and Safety Executive
Library and Information Services
Broad Lane
SHEFFIELD S3 7HQ
Telephone: (0742) 752539 Telex: 54556

Health and Safety Executive
Library Information Services
St Hugh's House
Stanley Precinct
Trinity Road
BOOTLE
Merseyside L20 3QY
Telephone: 051-951 4381 Telex: 628235

Health and Safety Executive
Library and Information Services
Baynards House
1 Chepstow Place
Westbourne Grove
LONDON W2 4TF
Telephone: 01-221 0416 or 01-221 0870 Telex: 25683

ISBN 0 11 883891 1

Introduction

1 This Guidance Booklet updates and revises the information formerly contained in TDN 30 *Safety in the use of rotating-table pie and tart machines* and also deals with the safeguarding of 'in-line' machines. While this publication deals specifically with the machinery hazards, the non-machinery risks, eg slips and falls due to product spillage, falls from inadequate work platforms and collisions with mobile trolleys etc, should not be overlooked.

Rotating-table machines

2 Accidents on these machines are common. The principal dangers are the trapping of fingers:

(a) between the top die and the mould, and

(b) at the measuring device or cut-off slide of the depositing mechanism.

3 A high standard of protection is necessary because of the number of hand operations, the fact that more than one person may be working on the machine, the automatic operation of the machine, and the need for thorough cleaning.

4 The most commonly used makes of machines are described below. The same principles should be used as a guide in safeguarding other makes of machine.

The Camwheat Universal machine

Guarding

5 The Universal machine has two working positions at the front and two at the rear. Pies complete with lids can be continuously produced as the machine has two pressing heads. The two pressing heads are guarded by two pairs of interlocking doors fitted with trip flaps at the bottom of each; two doors being at the front of the machine and two at the rear. The interlock switch for each pair of doors is of the 'Mobrey' magnetic type, and cam-operated limit switches are used for interlocking the trip flaps (Figs 1 and 1a).

6 The interlocking doors must be supplemented by an effective brake and, traditionally, a plain or ridged false table. The manufacturer now produces a safety frame which is a development of the earlier ridged base-plates and replaces the false table. The purpose of the false table or safety frame is to ensure that in the event of finger approach to the danger area the trip

mechanism on the doors is actuated to stop the machine.

False table

7 The doors and trip flaps must be adjusted as low as possible, ie until there is just working clearance between the top of the pie and the bottom edge of the flap. The false table is intended to maintain a minimal clearance on those parts of the table which are clear of the moulds and so prevent access to the traps beneath the dies. The false table must be of rigid construction and of the correct depth, the aim being to keep the top of the table as near as possible level with the top of the moulds; in this connection indents should be provided to permit easy removal of the moulds. It is essential that a false table or safety frame of the correct dimensions is used for each size of mould.

8 In recent years there has been a tendency to employ moulds and dies larger than were originally intended to be processed on the machine, in order to produce larger pies. This has resulted in the space between the edge of the trapping point and the trip flap being dangerously reduced. A ridged false table (Figure 1) was developed to improve safety in these circumstances and the manufacturer now supplies machines fitted with a safety frame, a device which has replaced the false table arrangement.

Safety frame

9 The safety frame is intended to overcome the risks inherent in failure to adjust guards correctly and to ensure safety when deep pies are processed. It consists of an inner ring at the centre of the rotating table and radial webs or upstands which extend across the table. A pie mould is located within each well formed by the radial webs; the webs are slightly higher than the pie mould to avoid pastry fouling the trip flaps. In practice it is normally necessary to have only one safety frame corresponding to the deepest pie moulds. In certain cases, another safety frame may be required for machines making large pies where it may be necessary to provide a stripper plate to stop pies lifting. It is not possible to fit such a stripper plate if the safety frame is significantly deeper than the pie

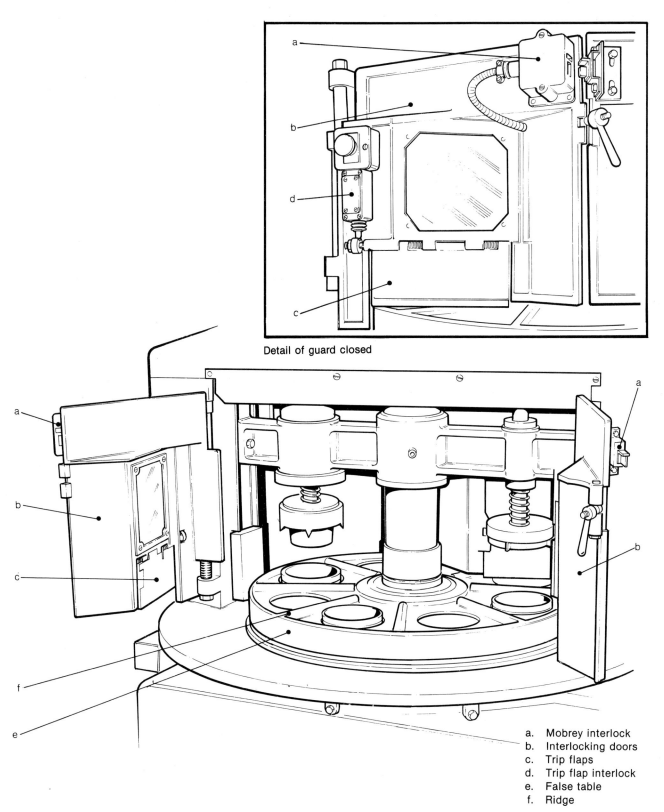

Detail of guard closed

a. Mobrey interlock
b. Interlocking doors
c. Trip flaps
d. Trip flap interlock
e. False table
f. Ridge

Fig 1 Camwheat Universal

moulds. The machine manufacturers will be able to give guidance on this feature.

10   The trip flaps on the doors have been modified so that the flap extends downwards to prevent access from the side. There is also a small roller tab on one trip flap which corresponds to machined cut-aways on the outer edge of the safety frame web. This arrangement ensures correct setting of the doors, for unless the roller passes through the cut-aways, the webs will fail, the roller tab will deflect the trip flap and the machine will stop.

11   A Universal machine fitted with a safety frame is shown in Fig 2. The motion of the table is intermittent, being synchronised with the stroke of the pressing head. The arrangements should be such that a radial web of the safety frame closes the gap beneath the trip flap as the

ceases to index prior to the downward movement of the pressing head, ie the web should be located vertically* beneath the trip flap when the indexing stops and the gap should not exceed 6mm. This timing is essential as it should ensure that if a hand is in a position of danger, the web will press the hand against the trip flap at a point in the cycle which will give sufficient time for the brake to arrest the downward movement of the head before trapping can occur.

---

*   The gates and trip flaps of the Universal machine are not quite radially symmetrical to the central machine axis. When the machine table comes to rest at the stroking position the webs of the safety frame are not directly below the trip flaps but have normally rotated slightly beyond the position of the trip flaps.

a.   Safety frame
b.   Trip flaps
c.   Roller tab
d.   Trip flap interlocks
e.   Emergency stop button
f.   Main doors' interlock

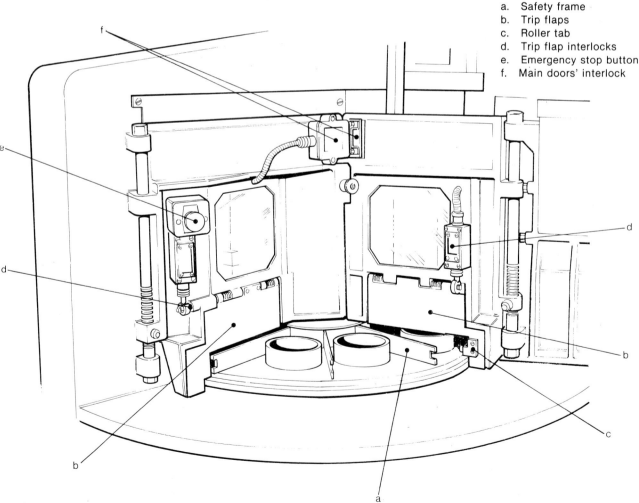

Fig 2   Camwheat Universal with safety frame

General precautions : Maintenance

12 Regular and proper maintenance is necessary to ensure the correct adjustment and functioning of guards and safeguards in this respect, the following points are particularly relevant:

(a) An effective brake is essential to ensure that the motion of the dies is arrested quickly once a trip flap has been deflected.

(b) The correct operation of the trip flaps should be checked regularly; eg at least daily. Operators should be trained to use the normal operational stop controls when they wish to stop the machine. They should not use a trip flap for this purpose; this should be regarded as an emergency stop.

(c) Minimal deflection of the trip flap must actuate the limit switch (ie not greater than 10mm at the lower edge). Excessive flap movement before actuation of the limit switch could allow a person's fingers to enter the dangerous trapping area before the machine has stopped.

(d) Periodic lubrication of the hinge pins for the trip flaps is necessary to ensure the continued free movement of the trip flaps and minimise corrosion of the hinge pins.

(e) The fixing devices securing the safety frame to the machine table should be checked for tightness to avoid free movement of the frame about the fixing points.

(f) The cutaway in each radial web of the safety frame should be well engineered such that the machine can be set with minimal clearance between the top edge of each web and the bottom edge of each trip flap (6mm maximum).

(g) The cutaways and roller tab should be checked for wear. The cutaway must not be filed or the roller tab removed to allow excessive or unrestricted upward movement of the doors.

(h) The radial webs should be checked for distortion and, where necessary, restored to their original profile/contour.

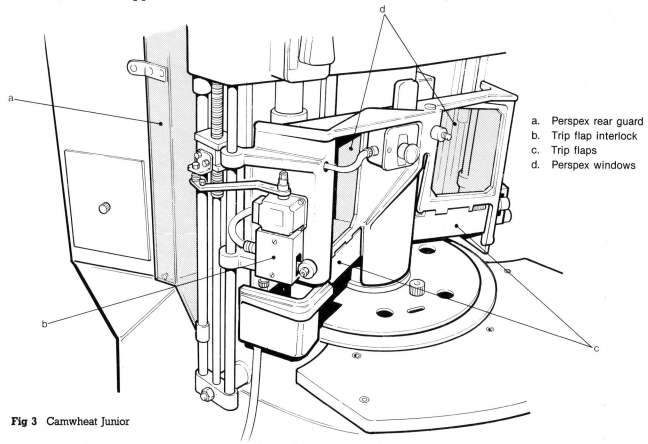

a. Perspex rear guard
b. Trip flap interlock
c. Trip flaps
d. Perspex windows

Fig 3 Camwheat Junior

The Camwheat Junior machine

13 The machine is shown in Fig 3 and is, as the name implies, a smaller version of the Universal machine, which is supplied fitted with a safety frame (not shown). The reciprocating blocking and lidding mechanisms are the same in principle as for the Universal machine.

14 The Junior machine is normally supplied with a soft meat depositor but it can be supplied with a pork meat filler similar to that fitted to the Universal machine. The machine can also be supplied without a depositor, in which case double doors are fitted front and rear.

15 The main guarding arrangements are similar to those found on the Universal machine. The machine is fitted with twin opening front doors with an interlocking trip flap at the bottom. These front and rear doors interlock by means of lever arm actuated limit switches. The gap between the left hand side of the machine frame and hopper/depositor is protected by a clear perspex guard panel. Guarding should be provided to prevent access to the blocking head through any gap which may exist at the rear between the depositor/filler and the central machine column.

The Peerless O'Matic Standard Machine

16 A piece of dough which has previously been placed in a tin or foil casing and put into the machine by hand is pressed into the shape of the mould and then filled to produce an unlidded pie or tart. Lidding is done on either a second machine, or on the same machine by running the unlidded pies through a second time with a lidding die substituted for the pressing die. In the lidding process a disc of dough, the lid, is placed over the mould by hand, the machine presses the lid into place trimming the surplus dough, and the completed pie within its tin or foil casing is removed by hand.

Guarding : traditional

17 The traditional type of guarding is illustrated in Figure 4, the guard being shown in the closed position. The rubber/plastic lower edge (a) of the hinged interlocking guard mounted above the machine table is capable of vertical adjustment. This lower edge should be set as close to the

top of the mould as practicable, ie the gap should be such as to just allow sufficient clearance for the pastry.

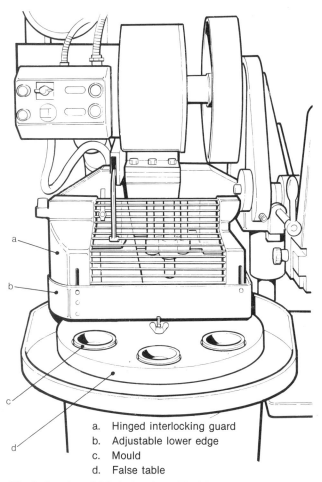

a. Hinged interlocking guard
b. Adjustable lower edge
c. Mould
d. False table

Fig 4 Peerless O'Matic Standard, Machine

18 Figure 5 illustrates a machine with the guard in the open position. Movement in either direction of the hinged front guard actuates a notched cam interlocking switch. The notched cam is either enclosed in a box, in which case it is operated by a link arm attached to the switch, or it is fixed directly to the guard. External cams should be properly secured (eg, be pinned or spot welded). This ensures that the machine cannot be started until the guard is fully closed. Any inward movement of the guard, as would happen should anyone attempt to pass a hand beneath the guard, results in the interlock operating, hence cutting off the power and automatically applying the brake.

Fig 5 Peerless O'Matic Standard, front guard open

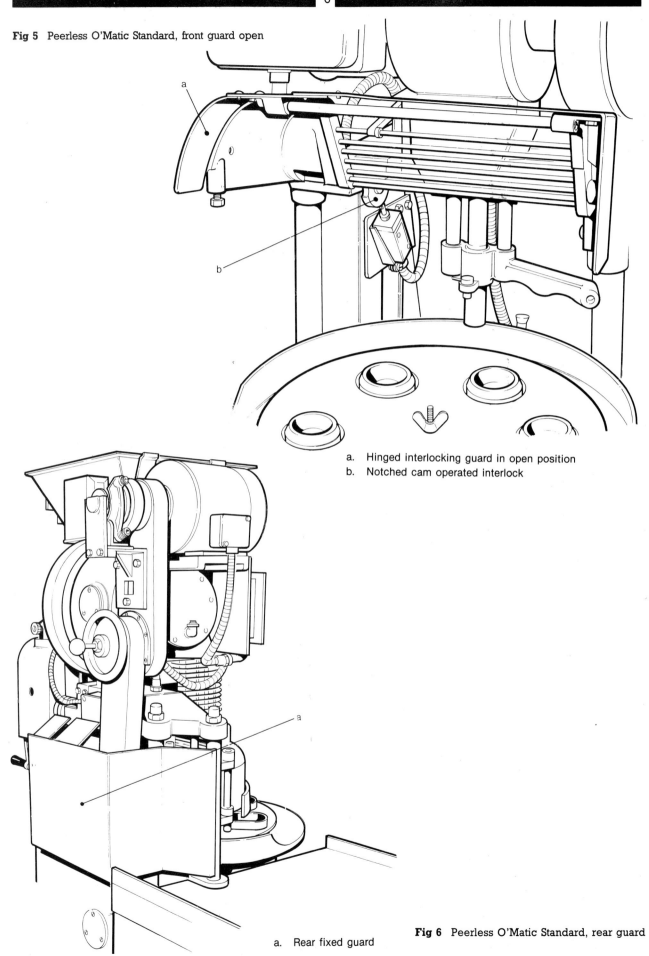

a. Hinged interlocking guard in open position
b. Notched cam operated interlock

a. Rear fixed guard

Fig 6 Peerless O'Matic Standard, rear guard

19 This method of interlocking is preferable to the magnetic interlocking switch provided on older models of this machine.

20 Figure 6 illustrates the type of fixed guard normally provided at the rear of this machine. Access is sometimes possible here through openings left in the guard to accommodate certain equipment, eg heater plugs for the pressing head or tubes from a filler, when this is no longer used. Such access should be prevented, by the provision of fixed plates attached to the rear of the guard, to cover these openings.

False table

21 A false table should be chosen such that the mould does not project more than 6mm above it. This height is considered to be sufficient for the removal of dough trimmings and should prevent finger access to the dangerous trapping area when the front guard is correctly set.

22 Figure 4 illustrates a typical false table and shows how the finger access zone for the removal of tins or foil casings is indented to prevent fingers being caught and dragged under the guard.

23 Separate false tables will be needed for differing pie sizes and it is essential that the appropriate false table is used.

Large pies

24 When large pies are being made some users find that the amount of dough needed results in insufficient clearance under the front guarding at the infeed side, causing fouling of the guard.

25 This can be overcome by the use of a modified front guarding arrangement. The standard adjustable piece is replaced by a similar piece with a portion cut away at the infeed side to allow greater clearance but with an extension attached to increase the horizontal distance between operator and the die. The adjustable piece of the guard should be robust, eg be made of metal.

26 Figure 7 shows this modified arrangement with the guard closed; Fig 8 illustrates how the front guarding has been cut back to allow greater clearance.

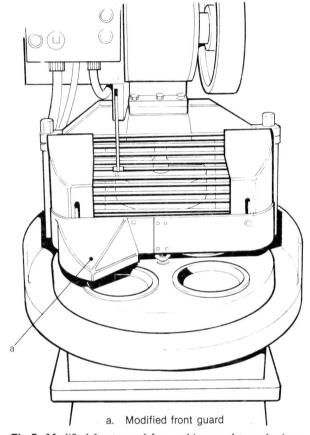

a. Modified front guard

Fig 7 Modified front guard for machine used to make large pies

Safety frame

27 The false table method of safeguarding cannot be used when deep pies are made or if the mould is used as a baking tin and is placed onto and removed from the machine table by the operator. One manufacturer has developed a safety frame to improve safety in these circumstances and machines now supplied are sometimes fitted with this guard arrangement.

28 The hinged interlocking guard remains across the front of the machine, similar to that shown in Fig 9. The adjustable edge has, however, been removed and replaced by a non-adjustable nose piece guard which comes down within 6mm of the mould locking plate at the central area of the machine and to within 6mm of the machine bed on its outer end and clear of the pie infeed and delivery openings (Fig 10). The nose-piece is then returned at right angles towards the rear of the machine to prevent access from the side. (Fig 9).

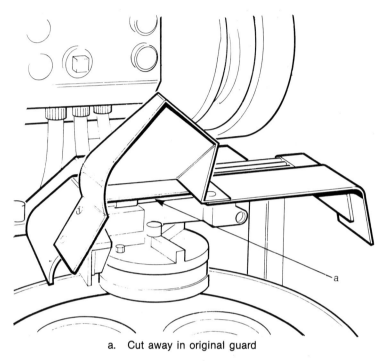

a. Cut away in original guard

Fig 8 Modified front guard for machine used for large pies open

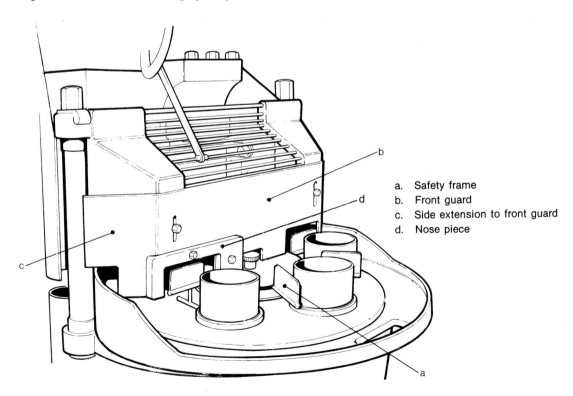

a. Safety frame
b. Front guard
c. Side extension to front guard
d. Nose piece

Fig 9 Peerless O'Matic Standard: front guard and safety frame

a. Safety frame
b. Front guard
c. Side extension to front guard
d. Nose piece

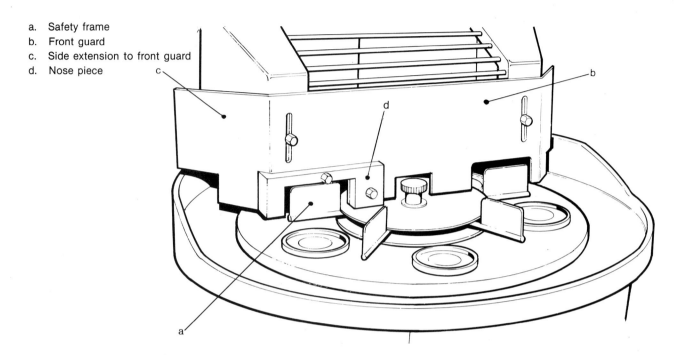

Fig 10 Close-up of nose piece

29 These machines are capable of processing a variety of shapes and sizes of pies, and different nose-pieces have been designed and produced to cater for the variations. Care must be taken to ensure that the appropriate nose-piece is being used. This method of safeguarding is not considered suitable for the processing of large diameter pies which prevent the use of the normal six stations on the rotating table.

30 When deep pies are being processed, the central mould locking plate is not used, the mould being retained on the machine bed by a special quick release locking method. In these cicumstances, the appropriate nose-piece should come down to within 6mm of the machine table in the area normally covered by the central mould locking plate.

31 The end result should be such that, when the appropriate nose-piece is located, clearance beneath the front guard does not exceed 6mm. The guarding must ensure that it will not be possible for the operator to reach through the pie infeed or delivery openings into the dangerous trapping area while the machine is running, without the following mould pressing his hand against the guard, so arresting the motion of the machine before injury can result.

Brake

32 On earlier models of this machine, the brake was applied to the rim of the flywheel. This was not satisfactory and the brake is now incorporated on the main drive (Fig 6). Users of old machines are advised to have this new type of brake fitted. The brake adjustment should be regularly checked to ensure continued efficient braking.

Peerless O'Matic Minor machine

33 This is a smaller machine intended for confectionery and small pie production. A side-hinged interlocking guard with an adjustable rubber lower edge is provided around the blocking head. (Fig 11). As with the standard machine it is necessary to use the appropriate false table.

34 Some models of the Peerless Minor machine were not fitted with a brake since it was thought that there was insufficient over-run to justify this. Experience has shown, however, that after appreciable usage the over-run on this model can be dangerous. Users are therefore advised to arrange for the fitting of a brake. The manufacturers can fit a brake on the motor, in

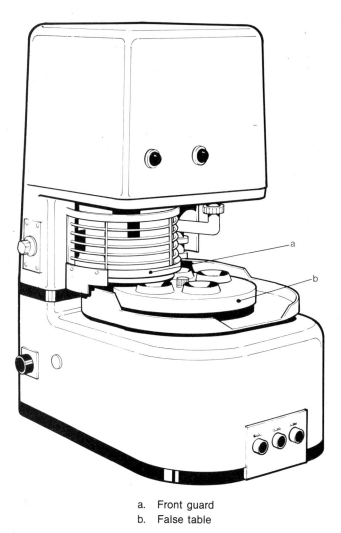

a. Front guard
b. False table

Fig 11 Peerless O'Matic Minor

the hollow chamber of the machine bed.

The Hunt machine

35 Hunt manufacture a rotating table machine which should be fitted with safety frames rather than false tables. Two frames are available: one for pies between 2in and 5in (50-125mm) diameter and another for pies between 5in and 6.75in (125-168mm) diameter. It is essential that the frame is positively located on the table, otherwise the frame could move relative to the indexing table and foul on the pressing head with resultant damage. The frame now incorporates a locating lug to supplement the centre securing screw to prevent movement of the frame relative to the table.

36 The machine is provided with a side-hinged front guard (Figs 12(a) 12(b)), fitted with a tongue and two adjustable pins. The striker locates in a switch mounted on the frame of the machine when the guard is closed, and depresses a shutter enabling the upper pin to enter the switch and make the circuit. If the guard is pushed towards the machine the lower pin, which is slightly shorter, should break the circuit.

37 Supplementary adjustable guards are fitted at the infeed and discharge points, each of which consists of a metal bracket to the front guard with a leather flap at the lower edge. These should be adjusted so that the gap between the lower edge of each flap and the surface of the pastry is restricted to a maximum of 6mm.

38 The flap at the infeed side can be hinged outwards and upwards. It carries a peg that ensures that the flap is down when the front guard is closed. The other flap is fixed in the vertical position. The leather flaps become supple with use and should be replaced before they allow access to the trapping zone.

The Waddell 'scotch pie' machine

39 This machine is shown in Fig 13. It has a four station rotating table with an electrically heated die moulding head and a trimming head. On the rotating table, the base of the mould is retractable. At the first station when the base of the mould is flush with the rotating table, a quantity of dough is pressed on top of the mould plate. As the table indexes round to the first position, the base of the mould retracts and forms a die for the moulding of the base of the pie. The heated die descends to mould the dough into the pie shell base. After the table has indexed to the next station, a trimming head descends to trim off any dough which is still left on the rotating table after the pie shell has been formed. At the next station the base of the mould remains in the lowered position to enable any scrap pastry to be removed from the table of the machine. When the table indexes round to the original position, the base of the mould rises to

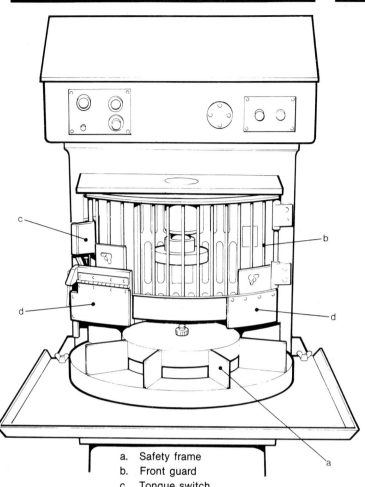

a. Safety frame
b. Front guard
c. Tongue switch
d. Supplementary guard

Fig 12(a) Hunt machine, front

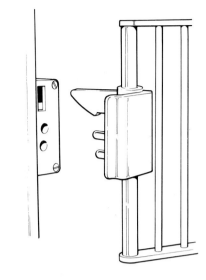

Fig 12(b) Interlocking switch

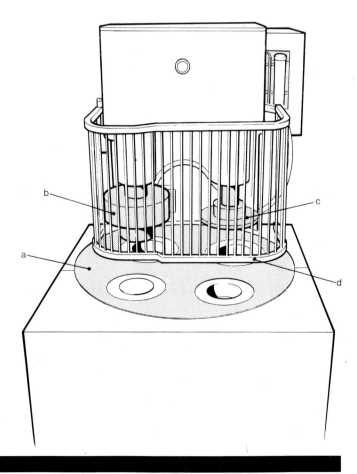

a. Rotating table
b. Moulding head
c. Trimming head
d. Hinged interlocked guard

Fig 13 Waddell 'scotch pie' machine

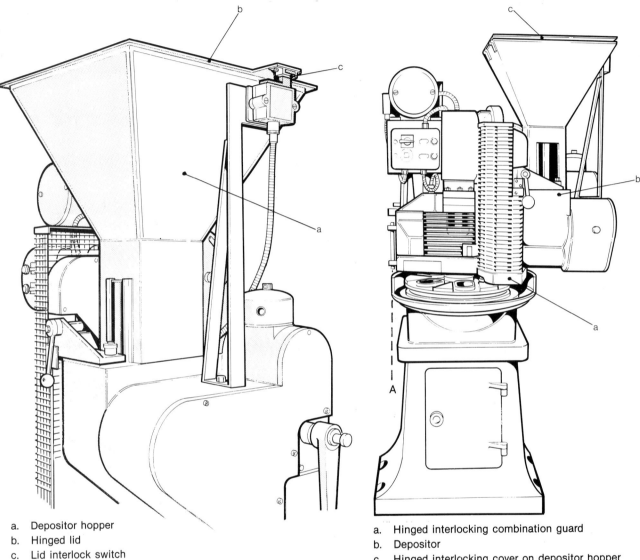

a. Depositor hopper
b. Hinged lid
c. Lid interlock switch

Fig 14 Depositor (side view)

a. Hinged interlocking combination guard
b. Depositor
c. Hinged interlocking cover on depositor hopper

Fig 15 Depositor (front view)

original position, the base of the mould rises to the table top position to enable the completed pie shell to be removed and a fresh piece of dough placed on the machine for the process to be repeated.

40   Access to the dangerous traps under the moulding head or trimming head as they descend is prevented by a hinged front interlocking guard which covers the rear part of the rotating table. The clearance between the bottom of the guard and the rotating table is fixed so that it is just sufficient for the dough placed on the rotating table to pass under the

bottom of the guard but not sufficient for anybody to reach under either head. The hinged guard is interlocked so that movement of the guard in either direction causes the power to be cut off and the machine to be brought to rest. If the guard is hinged right open an additional limit switch cuts off all power to the machine.

41   It is not necessary to have false tables or radial webs at this type of machine since the clearance between the rotating table and the guard is always constant. The dies remain hot for some time after the power is cut off and the operators should be warned of this danger.

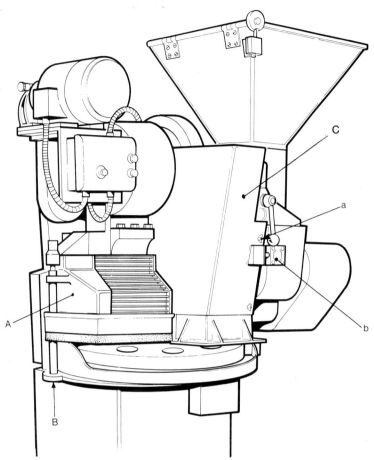

a. Wing nuts to fixing of depositor guard
b. Mobrey type interlock switch

Fig 16 Peerless Std, modified guards with depositor

Depositors

42 This section deals with a typical depositor; the principles of guarding shown are applicable to most makes of machine.

43 The depositor places a measured amount of material into the pie shell. The measuring mechanism is dangerous so access to it either down the feed hopper or through the discharge opening must be prevented.

44 Access down the feed hopper to the measuring or cut-off device at the base of the hopper can be prevented by means of a hinged interlocking cover as illustrated for a dry depositor in Figs 14 and 15. Alternatively access to the danger area can be prevented by fitting a hopper of sufficient length to prevent a person reaching the danger area.

45 Figure 16 shows a Peerless machine: guard 'A' prevents access to the die area, and guard 'C' to the depositor mechanism. Guard 'A' is provided with similar interlocks to those shown in Fig 4 and the method of operation is similar, except that the guard hinges about the vertical axis 'B'. Guard 'C', independent of guard 'A', is held in position by wing nuts and interlocked with 'Mobrey' magnetic switch, as it is necessary to remove the guard for cleaning and other purposes.

46 Figures 15 and 17 show a method of guarding adopted by the makers for a machine incorporating a dry depositor. The guard for the die area and that for the depositor cut-off zone are combined. This combined guard hinges about vertical axis 'A', is interlocked as shown in Fig 4, and obviates the need for an additional 'Mobrey' magnetic switch.

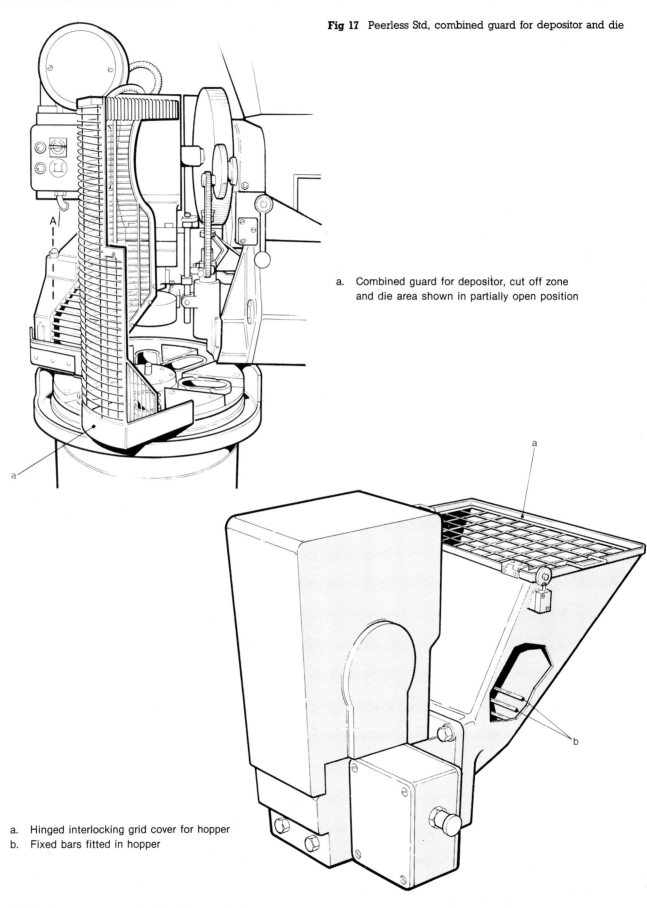

Fig 17 Peerless Std, combined guard for depositor and die

a. Combined guard for depositor, cut off zone and die area shown in partially open position

a. Hinged interlocking grid cover for hopper
b. Fixed bars fitted in hopper

Fig 18 Alternative method of feed hopper guarding

47 Figure 18 illustrates a 'wet depositor' with an interlocking cover to prevent access down the hopper. In cases where only 'wet' or fluid (soft) materials are used, fixed guard bars can provide an alternative to the interlocking cover.

48 On 'wet depositors' it has been found that the 'T' shaped discharge orifice supplied for older 'Peerless' machines is not adequate to prevent fingers coming into contact with the cut-off slide during cleaning. The makers now produce a longer 'T' piece and users are advised to have this fitted. Care should be taken to ensure that the two retaining screws are in position; these are a common feature on both the older and newer 'T' pieces and allow the unit to swivel but prevent its removal from the machine.

49 On certain of these 'wet depositors' there is a brass wing nut type plug, located under the depositor and to the rear of the discharge 'T' piece. This plug gives direct access to the internal moving parts. An extension tube which can be permanently attached to the machine to prevent such access is now fitted to new machines and is available from the maker for existing machines. Users are advised to check their machine and have the extension fitted if the above hazard exists.

50 The 'Camwheat Universal' machine normally has the depositor mounted inside the four interlocking doors (Fig 1) and these prevent operators gaining access to the depositor mechanism via the discharge orifice.

51 On older 'Camwheat Junior' machines access to trapping areas, formed by the depositor actuating mechanism and between die and mould, was possible via the opening in the vicinity of the depositor discharge. In addition, access to the depositor discharge port was possible when the discharge pipe had been removed for cleaning purposes. Such access should be prevented by a guard permanently attached to the existing interlocking door of the machine; the maker can supply such an extension guard. A fixed guard should prevent access to the depositor discharge mechanism and to the mould and die from the side of the depositor remote from the discharge pipe.

In-line pie and tart machines

52 Dangers associated with rotating-table machines are also found on in-line machines. In many cases the guarding principles detailed in earlier sections of this Guidance Booklet can be adopted.

53 The use of this type of machine is now becoming more widespread and various types are in use. While different makes may vary in detail, a typical machine is described here, and illustrated in Fig 19. Side drive chains carry foil trays or other containers through a sequence of machine stations which perform the various pie processes. The stations, which may be fixed or mobile, may include foil dispenser, bottom dough depositor, blocker, meat depositor, pastry divider, pastry sheeter, lid crimper and ejector unit.

54 Care should be taken to avoid secondary traps between the perforated moving belt and the guarding of the various stations. Where these exist, they can be eliminated by fitting shallow infills, just adequate for the pie depth beneath the belt at the intake to the station, or by providing trip flaps at the enclosure guards. (Fig 20).

Blocker and crimper units

55 There are dangerous traps at blocking and crimping units. Interlocking guards, or fixed guarding with interlocking access gates or panels, are normally provided at these units because of the frequency of access required.

56 Hinged side panels for pressing heads should be electrically interlocked, eg with a cam-operated limit switch as illustrated in Fig 79 of BS 5304: 1975, *Safeguarding of Machinery*. Where both pneumatic and electrical power are used the interlocking switch should be arranged to interrupt both services. Where necessary other interlocking methods should afford the same degree of protection.

57 It should not be possible to reach the dangerous trap created between the pressing head and pie tin or base plate via the infeed or discharge openings in the guarding. In this respect the size of the aperture and its distance from the dangerous area should conform with Fig 5 of BS 5304: 1975. Further it should not be possible to gain access to the bottom die from beneath the belt, or to the top die by reaching

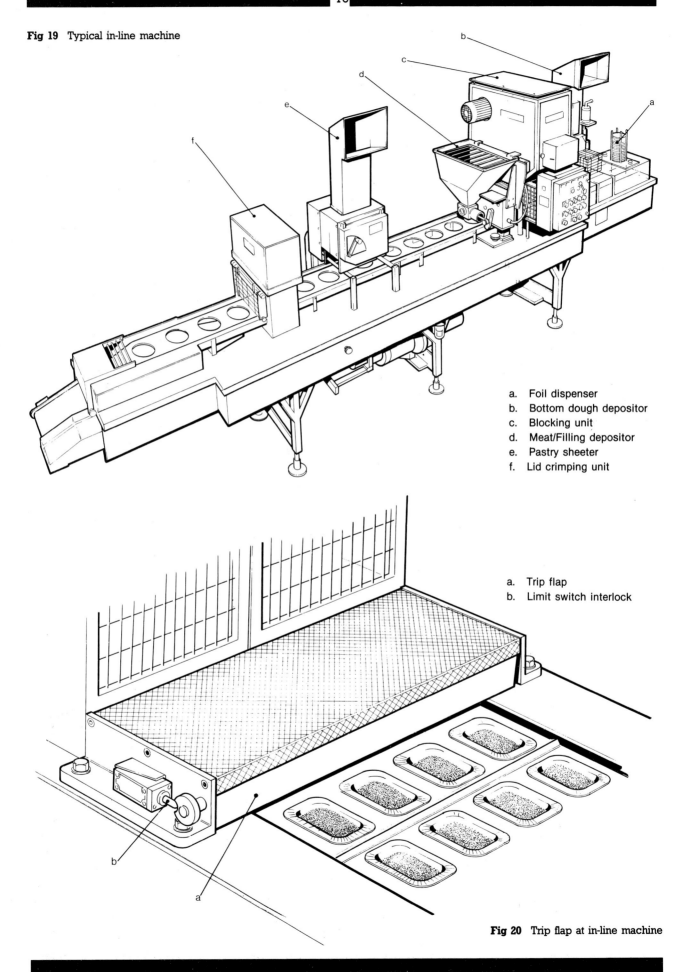

Fig 19 Typical in-line machine

a. Foil dispenser
b. Bottom dough depositor
c. Blocking unit
d. Meat/Filling depositor
e. Pastry sheeter
f. Lid crimping unit

a. Trip flap
b. Limit switch interlock

Fig 20 Trip flap at in-line machine

over the interlocking enclosure guard. A platform is sometimes provided alongside the machine for filling the meat or pastry hoppers and there have been accidents when employees standing on such platforms reached over the side guards and down into the dangerous traps. Thus it may be necessary therefore for the interlocking enclosure guard to be provided with fixed top guard panels.

Dough and meat depositor units

58 A similar unit performs each function. The material to be deposited is manually loaded into a feed hopper, it is then drawn down by two inrunning rollers and extruded out of an orifice into the pie tin in a cut-off device giving the required weight.

59 The depositor mechanisms are dangerous, so access down the feed hopper to the rollers, or to the discharge orifice and cut-off device must be prevented. Access to the rollers can be prevented by means of a swan-necked hopper, an extension hopper, or by a cover, in each case interlocked, or by fixed bar guarding. The cut-off device may be guarded by fixed or interlocking guards.

60 Further guidance on the guarding of depositors is contained in the preceding section dealing with rotating table machines.

Pastry divider and sheeter units

61 The pastry divider and pastry sheeter are normally three roll devices. The units run continuously, thus a loop of top paste sheet is formed to take up the index movement. The paste thickness is controlled and can be adjusted as required.

62 It should not be possible to gain access to the dangerous intakes created between the in-running rollers of either unit. An interlocking hopper is normally provided; guarding considerations are similar to those described for depositors.

Ejector units

63 A trapping risk can exist at the ejector discharge unit provided on some machines. Often this pushes pies on to a short horizontal

conveyor, where employees pack them into trays. Traps may be formed between the pusher plate and fixed parts of the machinery. One manufacturer has provided an interlocking tunnel guard over the pusher plate and has hinged the pusher plate at the rear so that it will fold up if an obstruction gets between the conveyor and the plate.

64 All conveyors associated with these machines should be provided with effective guarding for any dangerous intakes, eg between end drums or tensioning drum and the conveyor belts.

Guarding: transmission machinery

65 Guards should be provided to prevent access to all dangerous transmission machinery such as gears, chains and sprocket wheels, belts and pulley wheels and shafting.

66 These guards are normally fixed so that a tool is required for their removal. However, if frequent access is required, guard panels should be suitably interlocked.

Guarding: general considerations, adjustments and maintenance

67 In any consideration of machine guarding, reference may be made to the principles of British Standard 5304: 1975 *Safeguarding of Machinery*. As the purpose of guarding is to prevent access to any dangerous parts while it is in motion, it is essential that guards provided are of suitable design and of suitable construction.

68 Interlocking guards on all types of machines must be properly maintained and, where applicable, be properly adjusted to the correct height. Adjustable guards should be checked for correct setting daily and after each change of mould; they should also be tested daily to ensure that the interlocking arrangements and the brake are effective. Users should be alert to the fact that some of the bar guards provided at older machines can be easily distorted, allowing finger access. In such cases, stiffener rods should be fixed across the vertical or horizontal guard bars.

69 Some users have adopted a card record on each machine, the card being signed by the person setting and checking the guards at the beginning of each shift and at each die change.

70 It is particularly important that where there is frequent approach to the dangerous trapping area as with rotating table machines, a check is made to ensure that trip flaps can move freely and actuate the limit switch upon minimal deflection; and that appropriate false tables are used and are in good condition.

Interlocking switches

71 Reference has been made in this publication to the Mobrey switch. These were traditionally used on some makes of pie and tart machine guards, but no objection is taken to the use of other suitably designed interlocking switches of an appropriate standard.

Instruction, training and supervision

72 On some rotating table machines the system of false table and guard can be incorrectly assembled or set so as to give easy access to the dangerous parts. Similarly, where a number of different safety frames or fixed guards can be used at a machine, the incorrect one can be

fitted. It is therefore essential that **all** those who operate, clean or maintain these machines receive such instruction, training and supervision as is necessary to ensure their safety. During training, bad practices such as the use of trip flaps as operational stop controls, should be actively discouraged.

73 There is not the same frequency of approach to dangerous parts with in-line pie and tart machines. Nevertheless, the traps formed at these machines are capable of inflicting serious injury and thus attention to instructions, training and supervision is no less important.

74 Pie and tart machines are Prescribed machines as specified in the Schedule to the Dangerous Machines (Training of Young Persons) Order 1954. Section 21 of the Factories Act 1961 relating to the training and supervision of young persons, under 18 years of age, working at dangerous machines will apply.

75 Section 6 of the Health and Safety at Work etc Act 1974 (HSW Act) places a duty upon the manufacturer or supplier of a machine to provide adequate information in connection with its use to ensure that it is safe and without risks to health when properly used. Users should ensure that instructions as to the correct setting and safe operation of the machine are drawn up if these were not supplied with the machine.

Printed in the UK for HMSO C65 11/86